VILLAINS

COUNT DOOKU

The public leader of the Separatists, Count Dooku has persuaded many planets to leave the Republic and join the Confederacy of Independent Systems. Those worlds now supply fleets and droid armies to the Separatists for their fight with the Republic. Dooku was once a respected Jedi Master, but he left the Order and returned to his home planet of Serenno, where he reclaimed his noble title and family wealth. The Jedi mourned his departure, but they didn't know the real reason he'd left: Dooku had fallen prey to the dark side of the Force, and taken the Sith title Darth Tyranus.

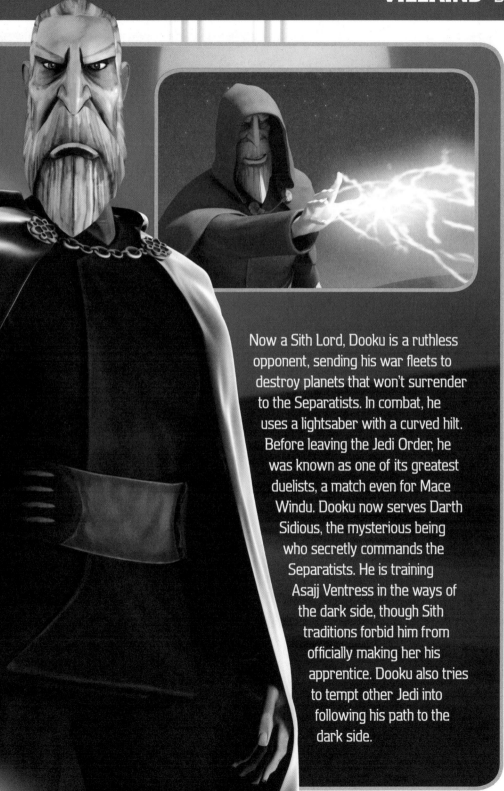

Now a Sith Lord, Dooku is a ruthless opponent, sending his war fleets to destroy planets that won't surrender to the Separatists. In combat, he uses a lightsaber with a curved hilt. Before leaving the Jedi Order, he was known as one of its greatest duelists, a match even for Mace Windu. Dooku now serves Darth Sidious, the mysterious being who secretly commands the Separatists. He is training Asajj Ventress in the ways of the dark side, though Sith traditions forbid him from officially making her his apprentice. Dooku also tries to tempt other Jedi into following his path to the dark side.

GENERAL GRIEVOUS

The savage commander of the Separatist military, Grievous is a cyborg—half living being and half machine. Little is left of his organic body except his head and internal organs. He hates droids, even though most of his armies are made up of them, and becomes enraged if anyone makes the mistake of thinking he is also a droid. Tough armor protects Grievous's living flesh, and his fast reflexes make him a terrifying enemy. He is not Force-sensitive, but uses lightsabers in combat. Grievous hates Jedi, and keeps a collection of lightsabers taken from the ones he has killed on the battlefield.

Grievous was once a warrior on the planet Kalee, where he led his people in many wars against their neighbors. After a terrible accident nearly killed him, he accepted an offer from the Separatists to be rebuilt as a cyborg. In return for help for his people, he agreed to command the Separatist military. Count Dooku often criticizes Grievous, wanting him to do more damage to the Republic's forces. This makes the general angry: How can he defeat the Republic when all Dooku gives him are battle droids? They're so useless in combat that Grievous sometimes gets frustrated and destroys them himself.

DARTH SIDIOUS

The secret leader of the Separatists, Darth Sidious is a Dark Lord of the Sith, an ancient order of Force-users who battled the Jedi centuries ago. The Jedi thought they had destroyed the Sith, but they had only gone into hiding, waiting for the chance to take their revenge. Now, Sidious knows that the time has arrived. In ancient times, there were many Sith, but they would refuse to work together and wind up fighting one another. So a Sith named Darth Bane established the Rule of Two: There would only ever be two Sith: a Master and an apprentice.

Darth Sidious's first apprentice was Darth Maul, a tattooed Zabrak who used a lightsaber with two blades. After Maul was killed by Obi-Wan Kenobi, Sidious took a new apprentice: the Jedi Count Dooku. Dooku now serves as the public leader of the Separatists, taking orders from his hidden Master. To Dooku's surprise, Sidious sometimes seems unconcerned or even pleased when the Separatists' plans don't work out, telling Dooku that things are going exactly as he wants them to. Dooku can only guess at Sidious's master plan for his war with the Jedi and the forces of the Republic.

The assassin Asajj Ventress looks like a living nightmare, with bone-white skin, cruel eyes, and twin lightsabers spinning in her hands. Asajj serves Dooku, and yearns to be accepted as his apprentice and a true member of the Sith. She imagines that defeating a Jedi such as Obi-Wan Kenobi will finally make her a full Sith. In combat, Ventress allows the dark side of the Force to fill her heart and mind, giving her enormous power. The dark side has allowed her to defeat Jedi such as Luminara Unduli, but Asajj is no match for more powerful Jedi such as Yoda.

ASAJJ VENTRESS

By the tme Count Dooku discovered Asajj, her thirst for vengeance had already put her on the path to the dark side. Asajj uses two sabers with curved hilts that were gifts from Count Dooku. She is a master of Jar'Kai, a two-handed fighting style. Her saber hilts can be joined together to make a two-bladed saberstaff. Obi-Wan and Anakin have fought Asajj several times, and worry her power will continue to grow.

CAD BANE

Some enemies of the Republic believe strongly that Dooku and the Separatists are right. But not Cad Bane—this fearless bounty hunter from the planet Duros is loyal only to credits. As long as Bane gets paid, he will take on any mission—and Bane is famous for always getting his prey. Bane is armed from head to toe with twin blasters, missiles, and weapons he keeps secret so he can surprise his enemies. Bane carefully researches each mission he's hired for, making sure he has the equipment he needs to succeed and get paid.

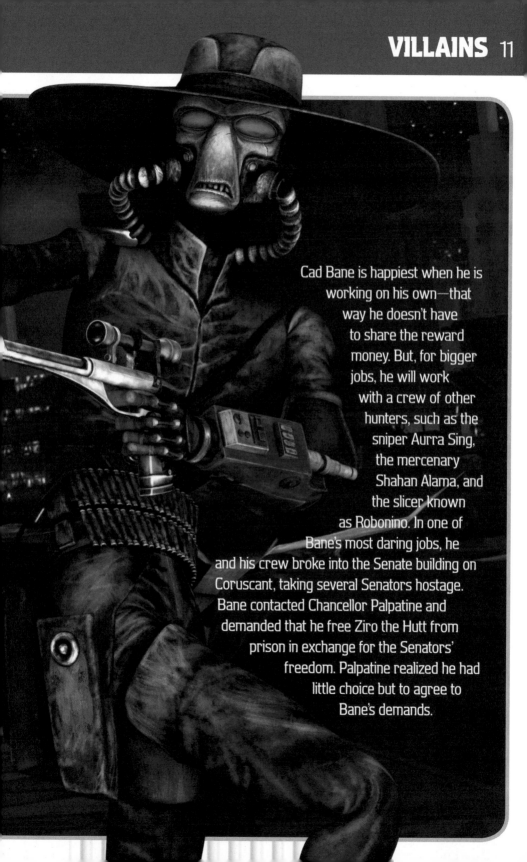

Cad Bane is happiest when he is working on his own—that way he doesn't have to share the reward money. But, for bigger jobs, he will work with a crew of other hunters, such as the sniper Aurra Sing, the mercenary Shahan Alama, and the slicer known as Robonino. In one of Bane's most daring jobs, he and his crew broke into the Senate building on Coruscant, taking several Senators hostage. Bane contacted Chancellor Palpatine and demanded that he free Ziro the Hutt from prison in exchange for the Senators' freedom. Palpatine realized he had little choice but to agree to Bane's demands.

NUTE
GUNRAY

A ruthless Neimoidian, Nute Gunray is the viceroy of the Trade Federation and a key member of the Separatist leadership. Years ago, Gunray pushed the Trade Federation into a trade dispute with the Republic, blockading the planet Naboo. That led to the Separatist movement, and the war that has now left the galaxy in ruins. The Naboo blockade was broken by Anakin Skywalker, then just a child. But Gunray has saved his hatred for Padmé Amidala, who fought his invasion and helped cause lots of trouble for Gunray in the Republic's courts. He dreams of the day he will have revenge.

Neimoidians compete furiously with each other from the day they are born. Grubs live together for the first seven years of their lives, and those who don't get enough food are allowed to die. So it's no surprise that Neimoidians remain greedy even once they become adults. In an effort to trap Padmé, Gunray blockades the planet Rodia until its Senator, an old friend of Padmé's, agrees to turn her over to the Trade Federation in return for food and supplies. But Padmé breaks out of prison and Gunray is marched off to pay for his crimes.

BATTLE DROIDS

The armies of the Separatists contain millions of these mechanical soldiers. B1 battle droids are simple machines designed to defeat their enemies not by being smart, but by attacking in huge numbers. Many Republic worlds have fallen to their blasters and now live in fear of the thud of their marching metal feet. Battle droids can be hacked apart with lightsabers or blown to bits by laser fire. Clone troopers are taught not to aim for the chest, which has thick armor. Instead, they fire at the weak spots: the joints where battle droids' arms and legs meet their bodies.

The first battle droids were controlled by a computer on a Trade Federation ship in orbit. But that meant if the ship were destroyed, the army would shut down and be useless. Since then, the Separatists have built simple electronic brains that let battle droids think on their own, though they're still not very smart. Clone troopers call their metal foes "clankers," and the droids can seem harmless or even funny, particularly when their droid brains struggle with a problem they can't solve. But when thousands of droids are marching toward Republic troops with their blasters raised, it's no laughing matter.

SUPER BATTLE DROIDS

The B1's big brothers are the B2 super battle droids—big, heavy mechanical killers with tough armor and laser cannons in their fists. Super battle droids aren't very smart, either, but they are much harder to destroy than the B1s, and both clone troopers and Jedi regard them with respect. In combat, super battle droids are very aggressive. Sometimes they shove their smaller B1 cousins out of the way to get closer to their enemies. Veteran clone troopers have learned that B2s can be tricked: Their droid brains sometimes forget about enemies they can no longer see.

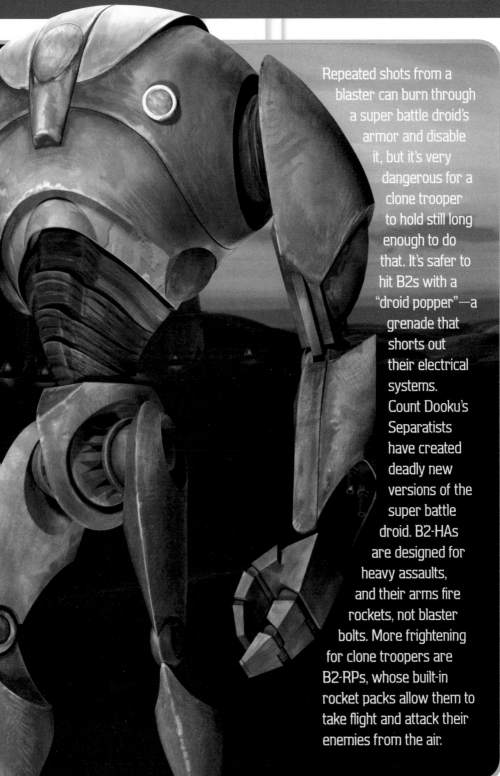

Repeated shots from a blaster can burn through a super battle droid's armor and disable it, but it's very dangerous for a clone trooper to hold still long enough to do that. It's safer to hit B2s with a "droid popper"—a grenade that shorts out their electrical systems. Count Dooku's Separatists have created deadly new versions of the super battle droid. B2-HAs are designed for heavy assaults, and their arms fire rockets, not blaster bolts. More frightening for clone troopers are B2-RPs, whose built-in rocket packs allow them to take flight and attack their enemies from the air.

The Separatists have many military units, but destroyer droids—sometimes called droidekas—are the ones that clone troopers fear the most. Droidekas roll along the ground at high speeds until they get near their targets. Then they uncurl, raise their energy shields, and open fire with their powerful cannons. Droidekas were designed and built by an insect species known as the Colicoids, who roll along the ground in the same way as the machines they built. The Colicoids sold droidekas to the Trade Federation, and then later to the Separatists for their war with the Republic.

DESTROYER DROIDS

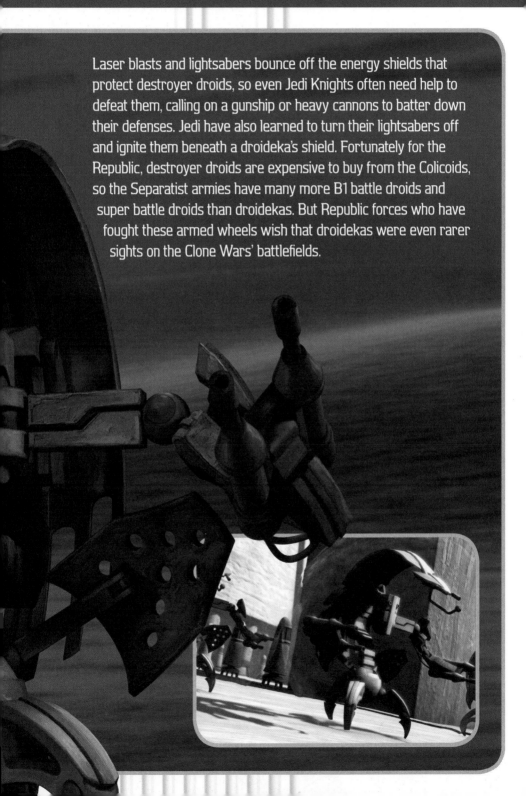

Laser blasts and lightsabers bounce off the energy shields that protect destroyer droids, so even Jedi Knights often need help to defeat them, calling on a gunship or heavy cannons to batter down their defenses. Jedi have also learned to turn their lightsabers off and ignite them beneath a droideka's shield. Fortunately for the Republic, destroyer droids are expensive to buy from the Colicoids, so the Separatist armies have many more B1 battle droids and super battle droids than droidekas. But Republic forces who have fought these armed wheels wish that droidekas were even rarer sights on the Clone Wars' battlefields.

MAGNAGUARDS

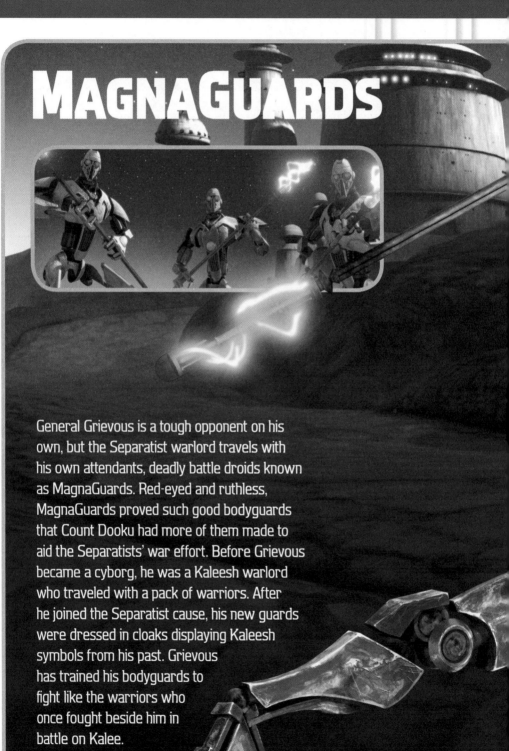

General Grievous is a tough opponent on his own, but the Separatist warlord travels with his own attendants, deadly battle droids known as MagnaGuards. Red-eyed and ruthless, MagnaGuards proved such good bodyguards that Count Dooku had more of them made to aid the Separatists' war effort. Before Grievous became a cyborg, he was a Kaleesh warlord who traveled with a pack of warriors. After he joined the Separatist cause, his new guards were dressed in cloaks displaying Kaleesh symbols from his past. Grievous has trained his bodyguards to fight like the warriors who once fought beside him in battle on Kalee.

The MagnaGuards were built by Holowan Mechanicals with reused parts from their line of IG lancer droids. But MagnaGuards have stronger armor, faster reflexes, and the ability to learn from their experiences in combat. They fight best with their electrostaffs, whose electric tips can stun or kill an opponent. MagnaGuards like to gang up on their opponents, spinning their electrostaffs in deadly circles and waiting for their enemies to make a fatal mistake. They can keep fighting even after their heads are cut off, an advantage that clone troopers and Jedi have discovered at the cost of their own lives.

A single battle droid isn't much of a threat to a clone trooper who's been trained well, so B1s fight their enemies by overwhelming them with numbers. It's a different story with the Separatists' new commando droids: They're tougher, faster, and much smarter than the "clankers" usually seen in battle. Commando droids use blasters and vibroswords and carry tools that let them pick locks, burn through doors, and invade computer systems. They can even imitate the voices of living beings, and do so in order to sneak into places where they don't belong, where they wreak havoc or ambush unsuspecting clone troopers.

COMMANDO DROIDS

One of the Republic's first clashes with commando droids came on the Rishi moon, where a squad of the sneaky droids broke into a military base set up to protect the space route to Kamino, the planet where clone troopers are born and trained to serve as Republic soldiers. At Rishi, commando droids gained control of the base's communications, and General Grievous prepared a fleet to invade Kamino. But a clone rookie named Hevy saved the Republic from disaster by sacrificing his own life to destroy the base, alerting Republic forces to the danger.

IG-86
ASSASSIN
DROIDS

The galaxy's rich and powerful often feel they need protection for themselves or their homes. To meet this need, Holowan Mechanicals created sentinel droids programmed to defend their owners and their property. But evil people soon realized the droids could be used for other things, such as getting rid of their enemies. IG droids were developed by a company called Phlut Design Systems on the planet Muunilinst. When Phlut failed to repay a loan from the InterGalactic Banking Clan, the IBC took over the firm, renamed the droids, and made them part of the Separatist war effort against the Republic.

On Muunilinst, clone troopers battled IG lancer droids armed with energy lances and riding swoop bikes. Ahsoka Tano and Anakin Skywalker fought two IG-86 units on the starship of the scavenger Gha Nachkt. And an IG droid named KRONOS-327 served Ziro the Hutt as an assassin. When Cad Bane invaded the Senate building on Coruscant, his gang of bounty hunters included a pair of IG-86 droids that served Ziro. Anakin Skywalker destroyed one of the droids despite the fact that he didn't have his lightsaber. The other droid helped free Ziro and escaped with the rest of Bane's band.

WHORM LOATHSOM

Whorm Loathsom is a general in the Separatist armed forces who has proved his bravery in battle against the Republic many times. On Christophsis, he led a column of Separatist tanks against the Republic defenses. If Christophsis were to fall, the Separatists would be free to invade a big chunk of the galaxy's Outer Rim. Loathsom is from Kerkoidia, and is angry that his people don't get the respect from other beings that they deserve. He thinks wars are noble, and those who fight them should respect each other, and not behave like savages. After all, most of the Clone Wars' victims are just droids and clones.

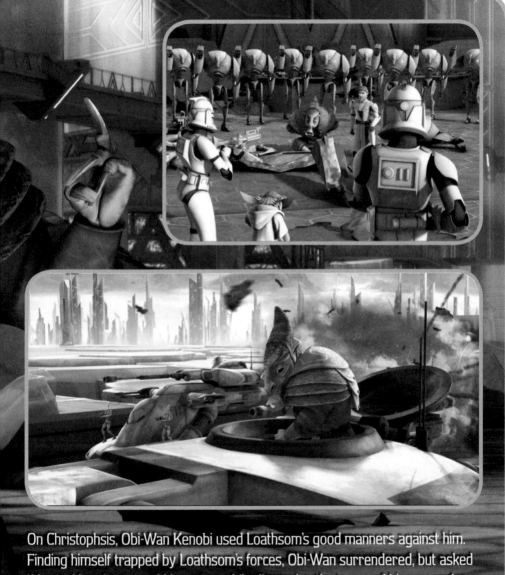

On Christophsis, Obi-Wan Kenobi used Loathsom's good manners against him. Finding himself trapped by Loathsom's forces, Obi-Wan surrendered, but asked if he and Loathsom could have tea while discussing the terms of his surrender. Whorm agreed, and Obi-Wan wasted so much time talking that Republic reinforcements had plenty of time to arrive and capture Whorm. Loathsom never went anywhere without LEP 96M3, his Coachelle Automata servant droid. 96M3 had learned to do things just the way Whorm liked them, from serving tea to bringing a message from Separatist leaders. The little droid was destroyed in the battle on Christophsis, and Whorm misses him very much.

LOK
DURD

Lok Durd is an arrogant and ruthless weapons designer who is always dreaming up new creations to destroy the enemies of the Separatists. Durd doesn't just think up weapons—he also tests them in the field, wanting to see for himself how they can be made even more deadly. Durd is a Neimoidian, and very proud of his species. He wears expensive silk robes whenever he can, and makes sure to look his best when humans are around. It makes him angry that a human is the public face of the Separatists, as everyone knows humans are inferior to Neimoidians.

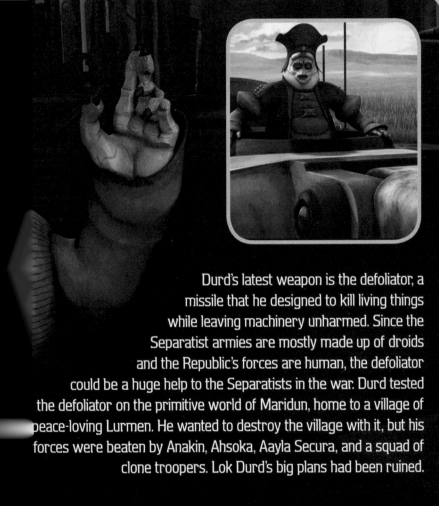

Durd's latest weapon is the defoliator, a missile that he designed to kill living things while leaving machinery unharmed. Since the Separatist armies are mostly made up of droids and the Republic's forces are human, the defoliator could be a huge help to the Separatists in the war. Durd tested the defoliator on the primitive world of Maridun, home to a village of peace-loving Lurmen. He wanted to destroy the village with it, but his forces were beaten by Anakin, Ahsoka, Aayla Secura, and a squad of clone troopers. Lok Durd's big plans had been ruined.

WAT TAMBOR

Wat Tambor is the foreman of the Techno Union, a group of companies that are always trying to make more complex gadgets. A die-hard supporter of the Separatist movement, Tambor has promised the Union's help with Count Dooku's war effort. As a reward, he has been named Emir of Ryloth, the homeworld of the Twi'leks. Tambor is from the planet Skako, which has an atmosphere of methane that is under very high pressure. When he isn't on Skako, he wears gear that lets him breathe and a metal suit. Without his suit, he would blow up and pop in the low pressure of other worlds.

The Separatists invaded Ryloth and have been very cruel to its people, stealing everything they own that is valuable and bombing their villages from their gunships. By treating the Twi'leks badly, they hope to show other planets of the Republic that it isn't a good idea to fight back against the Separatist droid armies. Tambor is very greedy, and wants to take all the Twi'leks' valuables for himself. He is so greedy that he refuses to leave the planet as the Republic's troops get closer and closer. It's a mistake: He is captured by the Jedi Knight Mace Windu and the Twi'lek leader Cham Syndulla.

AURRA SING

The feared bounty hunter Aurra Sing joins Cad Bane's crew in their attack on the Galactic Senate. Aurra is an expert with a blaster rifle, and serves as the team's sniper. When Senate Guards challenge Cad's group, she shoots several of them from a perch high up on one of Coruscant's skyscrapers. Aurra has dead-white skin, an antenna sticking out of her skull, long limbs, and a cruel smile. Her past is mysterious, and most people are too frightened of her to ask about it. But if you believe the rumors, she was once a Padawan in the Jedi Order.

STAR WARS

THE CLONE WARS

HEROES AND VILLAINS

FLIP BOOK

Written by Jason Fry

Grosset & Dunlap · LucasBooks

GROSSET & DUNLAP
Published by the Penguin Group
Penguin Group (USA) Inc., 375 Hudson Street, New York, New York 10014, USA
Penguin Group (Canada), 90 Eglinton Avenue East, Suite 700, Toronto, Ontario M4P 2Y3,
Canada (a division of Pearson Penguin Canada Inc.)
Penguin Books Ltd, 80 Strand, London WC2R 0RL, England
Penguin Group Ireland, 25 St. Stephen's Green, Dublin 2, Ireland
(a division of Penguin Books Ltd.)
Penguin Group (Australia), 250 Camberwell Road, Camberwell, Victoria 3124, Australia
(a division of Pearson Australia Group Pty. Ltd.)
Penguin Books India Pvt. Ltd., 11 Community Centre, Panchsheel Park, New Delhi—110 017, India
Penguin Group (NZ), 67 Apollo Drive, Rosedale, North Shore 0632,
New Zealand (a division of Pearson New Zealand Ltd.)
Penguin Books (South Africa) (Pty.) Ltd., 24 Sturdee Avenue,
Rosebank, Johannesburg 2196, South Africa

Penguin Books Ltd, Registered Offices:
80 Strand, London WC2R 0RL, England

This book is published in partnership with LucasBooks, a division of Lucasfilm Ltd.

The scanning, uploading, and distribution of this book via the Internet or via any other means without the permission of the publisher is illegal and punishable by law. Please purchase only authorized electronic editions and do not participate in or encourage electronic piracy of copyrighted materials. Your support of the author's rights is appreciated.

The publisher does not have any control over and does not assume any responsibility for author or third-party websites or their content.

ISBN 978-0-448-45391-0   10 9 8 7 6 5 4 3 2

HEROES

ANAKIN SKYWALKER

The Jedi Knights have defended the Galactic Republic for thousands of years. But now the Jedi are at war with the Separatists and their droid armies, led by the evil Sith Lord Count Dooku. The greatest hero of the Jedi Knights is Anakin Skywalker, who grew up on Tatooine as a slave and learned the ways of the Force as Obi-Wan Kenobi's Padawan learner. Anakin is an expert pilot, a genius at working with machines, and a mighty warrior when armed with his lightsaber. He has also taken a Padawan of his own, the young Togruta Ahsoka Tano.

While Anakin is a powerful Jedi, Obi-Wan and the ancient Jedi Master Yoda worry about him. Anakin loves his friends, and the Jedi teach that strong emotions can prevent a Jedi from making the right decisions to keep the galaxy safe. And an ancient Jedi prophecy suggests Anakin is the Chosen One who will bring balance to the Force. Obi-Wan and Yoda hope that being Ahsoka's master will teach Anakin the need to let his loved ones go. But they don't know that he loves Padmé Amidala, the Senator from the planet Naboo, and has secretly married her.

AHSOKA TANO

Ahsoka Tano is a Togruta, a species known for their red and white skin and striped montrals and head-tails. The ancestors of the Togruta were predators, and Togruta are known for their quick reflexes. During the Battle of Christophsis, the Jedi Council assigns Ahsoka to Anakin Skywalker as his Padawan. Ahsoka is brave, but she sometimes gets herself into trouble because she doesn't think before she acts. She knows she has a lot to learn, and hopes Anakin will help her do that. But Anakin has always said an apprentice would just slow him down, and at first he doesn't want to be Ahsoka's teacher.

Ahsoka proves herself to her new master on Christophsis, Tatooine, and Teth, and the two soon form a strong bond. She calls him "Skyguy," and he calls her "Snips." She also earns respect from Rex, the stern captain of the clone troopers who report to Anakin. But Ahsoka still makes mistakes, and knows there is a lot she has to learn if she is ever to become a Jedi Knight. The only way for her to learn these lessons is through experience, and with the Clone Wars tearing apart the galaxy, she will have plenty of opportunities to get it.

YODA

Yoda is the Grand Master of the Jedi Order, and has trained younglings and Padawans for nearly eight hundred years. Age has slowed him, forcing him to use a walking stick to get around, and few of the Padawans he teaches have any idea just how powerful he is with the Force. Yoda rarely uses his lightsaber now, but when he does he is a terrible enemy, able to spin and leap almost faster than the eye can follow. He can also call on the Force to do incredible things. As he likes to tell his younglings: "Size matters not."

During the Clone Wars, Yoda directs the Jedi and gives advice to Supreme Chancellor Palpatine, the leader of the Republic. In an attempt to save the Republic, he has agreed to put Jedi Knights in command of Republic troops and warships. But he worries that going to war will change the Jedi and make them forget their ancient promise to always serve the cause of peace. Yoda is also troubled by strange currents in the Force. He is worried about the fate of Anakin Skywalker, and afraid that the dark side of the Force has grown more powerful.

OBI-WAN KENOBI

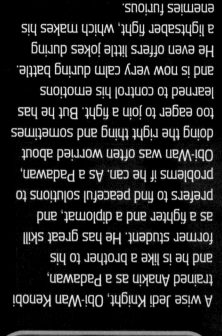

A wise Jedi Knight, Obi-Wan Kenobi trained Anakin as a Padawan, and he is like a brother to his former student. He has great skill as a fighter and a diplomat, and prefers to find peaceful solutions to problems if he can. As a Padawan, Obi-Wan was often worried about doing the right thing and sometimes too eager to join a fight. But he has learned to control his emotions and is now very calm during battle. He even offers little jokes during a lightsaber fight, which makes his enemies furious.

Obi-Wan's Master, Qui-Gon Jinn, was killed by a Sith warrior, and as he died he asked Obi-Wan to promise he would teach Anakin the ways of the Force. He kept his promise, but worries that Anakin is reckless, and will get himself in trouble either by rushing into battle or by being caught up in emotional attachments to others. Though he is no longer Anakin's master, Obi-Wan still watches out for his friend, trying to teach him to calm himself and think before he acts. Obi-Wan hopes being Ahsoka's teacher will help Anakin, but he worries that the two are so similar that they will only make each other's bad habits worse.

R2-D2

R2-D2 is an astromech droid whose job is to assist fighter pilots during space combat. R2 can repair damage, help pilots jump to hyperspace, and target enemy ships. R2 usually flies with Anakin, and the Jedi has learned to trust the little droid with his life, even refusing to erase R2's memory as part of normal maintenance. R2 is brave, loyal, and very stubborn. He sometimes acts as if he's a very short battle droid, taking on opponents with his electric prod, saw, and other tools. Sometimes his bravery gets him into trouble, but he has rescued his friends from many dangerous situations.

R2 has many arms, tools, and components inside his barrel-shaped metal body. He can get information from computers, use his holoprojector to play back messages, and even has rocket thrusters that allow him to fly—as long as they have enough fuel. R2's previous owner was the Royal House of Naboo, but he has known Anakin since the young Jedi was just a boy on Tatooine. When Anakin married Padmé, she gave the droid to him as a wedding gift, hoping R2 would keep her husband safe. R2 enjoys teasing Padmé's golden protocol droid, his friend C-3PO.

C-3PO

C-3PO is a protocol droid who speaks more than six million languages, which is a big help to his mistress, Padmé Amidala, in her work for the Galactic Senate. He is very fussy about etiquette and about his shiny golden finish, which he likes to keep looking its very best. C-3PO is not programmed for battle, and the thought of being in the middle of a fight scares him. He is often very worried about the safety of his friends and most of all himself, and gets frustrated when his friends don't listen to his warnings to be careful.

Anakin Skywalker built C-3PO as a gift for his mother out of old parts, and the droid spent several years on a Tatooine moisture farm before leaving with Anakin in an attempt to save Obi-Wan Kenobi on Geonosis. Anakin then gave C-3PO to Padmé to help her communicate with aliens from many worlds. C-3PO may not be brave, but he is loyal to Padmé and her friends, and tries to help out whenever he can. He is often impatient with the clumsy Jar Jar Binks and the rude, impatient little droid R2-D2, but that's mostly because he worries they'll get into trouble.

CLONE CAPTAIN REX

The leader of the famed 501st Battalion of clone troops, Rex is second in command to Anakin Skywalker. He is a brave soldier who makes tough decisions calmly and never backs down from a fight. Even when the odds are against him, Rex knows it's important to do his job. Rex can use many weapons, but prefers to fight with a blaster pistol in each hand. In battle he is protected by his white clone armor and by a flexible skirt called a kama. His helmet is marked by blue "jaig eyes," an honor given to soldiers for bravery on the battlefield.

Rex shares the same genetic makeup with the other clones who serve the Republic, and, like them, he was born in a vat on the planet Kamino and aged more quickly than a normal human. Kamino's cloners saw his ability to think well and lead troops in battle, and picked him to receive special training. Like many clone officers, Rex is known by a nickname he chose for himself. His unit number is CC-7567. Unlike most clones, Rex won't share why he picked his nickname. It's his secret, kept private even from the Jedi generals he serves faithfully.

COMMANDER CODY

Cody is second in command to Obi-Wan Kenobi, and has fought in many battles against the Separatists and their feared droid armies. He is more careful than Rex, who has been influenced by Anakin's reckless approach to fighting the enemy. Cody's unit number is CC-2224. Like Rex, the Kaminoans chose him for special training to lead other clone troopers. Cody wears armor with orange stripes, a symbol of the 212th Battalion that he leads. For a while he went on secret missions with an elite unit of clones, and has kept some of the special gear he used during those missions.

Cody is a smart strategist and an expert warrior who will use his blaster rifle or even a swift kick to disable a battle droid that's threatening the men who serve under his command. Under his helmet, his face is scarred by injuries suffered earlier in the war. Cody and Rex have served together in a number of battles. Like Obi-Wan and Anakin, they have become friends, and Cody worries about Rex the same way Obi-Wan frets about Anakin. Rex has a habit of rushing into danger when Cody thinks it would be smarter to wait and think about the situation.

MACE WINDU

One of the Jedi Order's champions, Mace Windu is a grim, intense warrior with an icy stare and little tolerance for disobedience in the ranks of the Jedi. Mace believes in absolute loyalty to Jedi traditions, and he has trouble trusting Jedi who question the decisions of the Jedi Council. Mace is famous for his unique, purple-bladed lightsaber, and for his ferocity in battle. He is a master of the Vaapad combat style, which is quick, deadly, and so aggressive that it forces a Jedi who uses it to come dangerously close to the dark side of the Force.

Mace is particularly suspicious of Anakin Skywalker. He knows Anakin has a good heart and believes strongly in the Jedi way, but he opposed the decision to train Anakin as a Jedi, thinking he was too old to be taught how to control his emotions. Mace fears that Anakin's passions will cause him to fail to do his duty, and worries that the Jedi may have misread the prophecy that Anakin will bring balance to the Force. The dark side has clouded the Jedi's ability to see the future, and Mace worries that evil days await both the Order and the Republic.

KIT FISTO

Kit Fisto is a Nautolan Jedi Master from the planet Glee Anselm. Younglings love his gentle ways and his broad smile, but they don't know that the Jedi with the green skin and the black eyes has fought many battles against some of the galaxy's most evil beings. Kit can breathe both air and water, and carries a special lightsaber that will work underwater. Nautolans are superb swimmers, and Kit enjoys fighting in the water, shedding his heavy Jedi robes and boots so he can dive and twist gracefully beneath the waves.

Nautolans' head tentacles give them an excellent sense of smell. They can detect pheromones released by beings who are feeling strong emotions. This can give them a big advantage in combat and when they are negotiating a treaty or some other bit of galactic diplomacy. Kit has trained a number of Padawans, and he is close to former students such as Bant Eerin and Nahdar Vebb. But he worries about the Order's younger Jedi, fearing that coming of age during a time of war will cause them to forget that a Jedi's first job is to keep peace in the Republic.

PADMÉ AMIDALA

Padmé Amidala is the young Senator from the lush green planet of Naboo, and the secret wife of Anakin Skywalker. She was a voice for peace before the Clone Wars, but understands you can't negotiate with Count Dooku's droid armies. Padmé avoids violence when she can, but is a good shot with a blaster when she has to use one. The people of Naboo elected Padmé as their queen when she was just fourteen, shortly before the Trade Federation invaded their planet. She escaped and helped capture Nute Gunray, then agreed to serve in the galactic Senate when Naboo's new queen asked her to.

Padmé is kind and patient, and tries to see the good in people whenever she can. Her old friend Chancellor Palpatine has urged her not to be too trusting, fearing that those who claim to want peace will take advantage of Padmé's nature. Padmé loves Anakin, and it saddens her that their marriage must be kept a secret, and that the war rarely allows them to be together. Padmé dreams that when the war is over, she and Anakin will find a way to return to Naboo and live out their lives in peace and quiet.

JAR JAR BINKS

The Gungan Jar Jar Binks is a representative to the Senate from Naboo, and helps his longtime friend Padmé with her diplomatic duties. Jar Jar is clumsy and his ideas aren't always good. But he is kind and will do anything he can to help his friends. Jar Jar has had a remarkable life. He was banished from the city of Otoh Gunga for causing accidents, and traveled with Obi-Wan Kenobi and Qui-Gon Jinn when the Trade Federation invaded Naboo. He helped Padmé make peace with the Gungans and fought in the battle to free the planet.

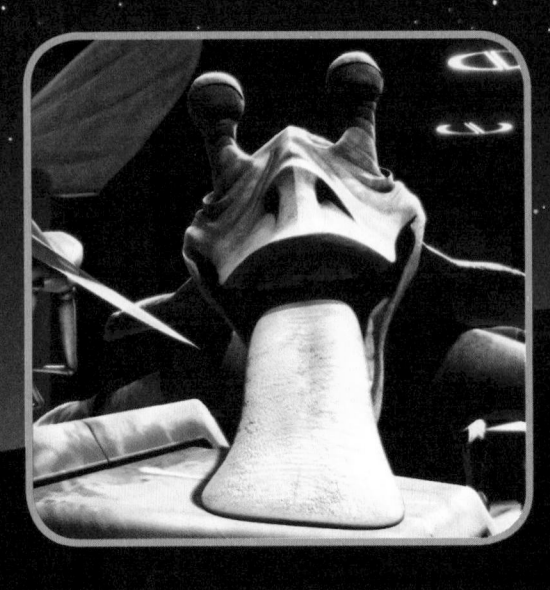

Gungans' flexible skeletons allow them to twist their bodies in ways other beings can only imagine. They can breathe both air and water and, though they can look awkward on land, in the water they are very graceful swimmers. Jar Jar never means to do any harm, but when he's around, accidents just seem to happen. Yet Jar Jar always manages to escape the chaos he causes, and sometimes his accidents give him a chance to rescue his friends and defeat their enemies. Padmé has learned not to be surprised—when Jar Jar is around, you never know what is going to happen.

LUMINARA UNDULLI

A near-human Jedi from the planet Mirial, Luminara is a stern teacher who believes that a Jedi must always keep control of his or her emotions and never allow passions to interfere with a mission. She wears the tattoo of the Mirial Adepts, an honor that is only given to the wisest warriors. Luminara is an expert at getting captured enemies to reveal their secrets, using not only the Force but also patient questions to break down a prisoner's defenses. When Nute Gunray is captured on Rodia, the Jedi Council sends her to interrogate him, hoping he will reveal the Separatists' secrets.

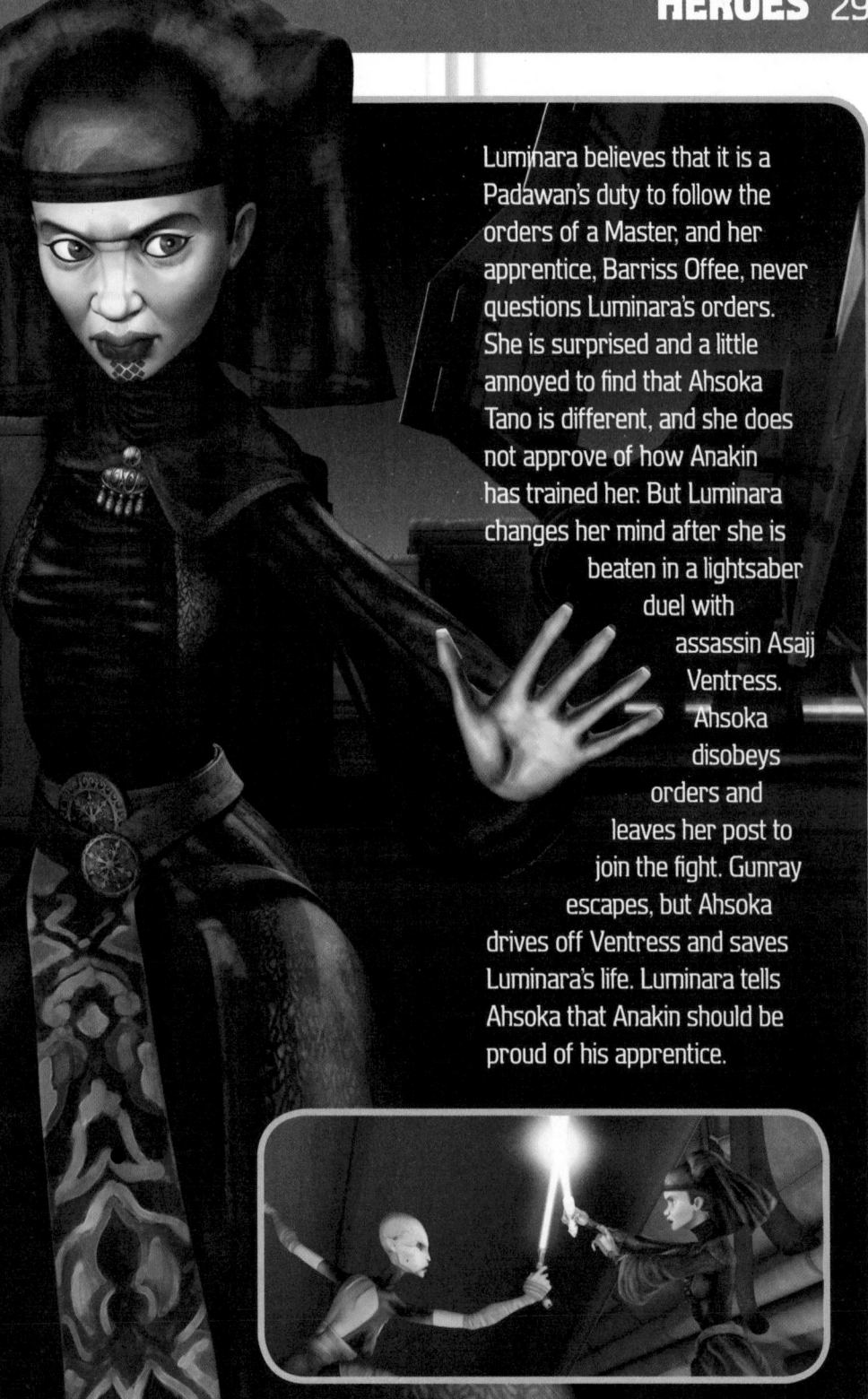

Luminara believes that it is a Padawan's duty to follow the orders of a Master, and her apprentice, Barriss Offee, never questions Luminara's orders. She is surprised and a little annoyed to find that Ahsoka Tano is different, and she does not approve of how Anakin has trained her. But Luminara changes her mind after she is beaten in a lightsaber duel with assassin Asajj Ventress. Ahsoka disobeys orders and leaves her post to join the fight. Gunray escapes, but Ahsoka drives off Ventress and saves Luminara's life. Luminara tells Ahsoka that Anakin should be proud of his apprentice.

PLO KOON

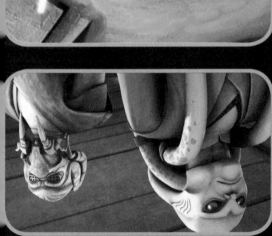

Plo Koon is a Jedi Master from the planet Dorin. He is an expert starfighter pilot and a wise warrior who cares for the clone troopers under his command, instead of seeing them as living droids to be thrown into battle without concern for their lives. Dorin's atmosphere contains little oxygen. To survive on a planet like Coruscant, Plo must wear a breathing mask to keep him from suffering oxygen poisoning and goggles that shield his eyes from harm. But he has some advantages. His skin is very tough, and Plo can even survive in the vacuum of outer space for some time.

Plo Koon's species is known as the Kel Dor. They have a strong sense of right and wrong, and think those who commit evil deeds deserve harsh punishments. Plo comes from a long line of Kel Dor Jedi, and is very proud of this tradition of service. Plo discovered Ahsoka Tano's abilities with the Force when she was a baby, and brought her to the Jedi Temple to be trained. He has looked after the girl he calls "Little Soka" for her entire life, and worries that Anakin Skywalker is too reckless to be a good teacher for her.

AAYLA SECURA

A blue-skinned Twi'lek, Aayla Secura is an athletic, confident Jedi Knight who has been in many battles. She does not wear the robes of a Jedi, preferring clothing that leaves her arms and legs free in case she has to fight. Aayla was saved from life as a slave by the Jedi Quinlan Vos, who made her his Padawan. She has struggled with emotional attachments and a desire to take revenge on those who treated her badly. She sees that Ahsoka has the same problems, and tries to teach the young Padawan how to stop her emotions from controlling her actions.